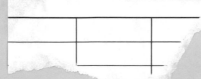

Date Due

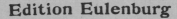

Edition Eulenburg

No. 507

SCHUBERT

Symphony, No. 4
(Tragic)
C minor–Ut mineur--C moll

Ernst Eulenburg, Ltd., London-Zürich

Made in England

Eulenburg Miniature Scores

CHAMBER MUSIC

Edition Eulenburg

SYMPHONY, No. 4

C minor

(tragic)

by

FRANZ SCHUBERT

Composed 1816

First performed 19th November, 1849 at Leipzig, Musical
Society Euterpe, A. F. Riccius conducting.

With Foreword by Hermann Grabner

Ernst Eulenburg, Ltd.,
36-38, Dean Street, London, W. 1

SCHUBERT, SYMPHONY № 4, C MINOR

Schubert completed this symphony on April 27th 1816 in Vienna. The first performance was given on November 19th 1849 at a concert held by the "Euterpe" Musical Society.

The work is called the "Tragic" Symphony. This title was added afterwards, and not without reason, for, after the first three joyful symphonies, the first movement of the fourth breathes a spirit of sorrow and resignation, though not maintained for long. Both the first and last movements begin in C minor, and pass over, after somewhat monotonous and poorly contrasted figures in eighths, into the final section in C major, whilst the two middle movements, the Andante in A flat and the Minuet in E flat bear but slight resemblance to the tragic mood. These two movements, therefore, are the most important, the Andante containing some entrancing melody, the quiet principal theme being well contrasted with the more animated middle section.

Prof. Hermann Grabner

SCHUBERT, SYMPHONIE № 4, C Moll

Schubert vollendete diese Symphonie am 27. April 1816 in Wien. Die Erstaufführung erfolgte am 19. November 1849 im ersten Konzert der Musikgesellschaft „Euterpe".

Die Symphonie trägt die Bezeichnung „tragische", die Schubert dem Titel nachträglich hinzufügte, nicht mit Unrecht. Nach den lebenslustigen Symphonien Nr. 1, 2 und 3 schlägt namentlich der erste Satz dieses Werkes Klänge tiefster Schwermut und Resignation an, ohne freilich die düstere Stimmung auf die Dauer festzuhalten. Denn sowohl der erste Satz wie das Finale, die beide in C-Moll beginnen und in ihrer wenig kontrastreichen Achtelbewegung etwas monoton wirken, schwingen sich zum Schluß zu befreiendem C-Dur auf, während die beiden Mittelsätze, das Andante in As-Dur und Menuett in Es-Dur, nur vorübergehend eine tragische Stimmung aufkommen lassen. Diese beiden Sätze repräsentieren denn auch die bedeutend wertvolleren Partien des Werkes, namentlich ist das Andante von einer bezaubernden Melodik und in seiner kontrastreichen Gegenüberstellung des ruhigen Hauptthemas in As-Dur und des bewegten Mittelsatzes in F-Moll von vollendeter Formschönheit. Wie sinnvoll steigert Schubert die Bewegung gegen Schluß durch die Verwebung der Sechzehntelfigur mit dem Hauptthema!

Prof. Hermann Grabner

Symphony, No. 4

I

Adagio molto

Franz Schubert
1797-1828

Ernst Eulenburg Ltd., London-Zürich

Allegro vivace

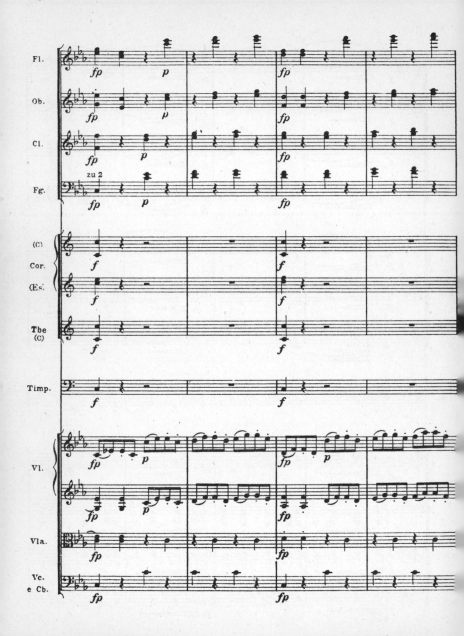

10

12

20

27

II

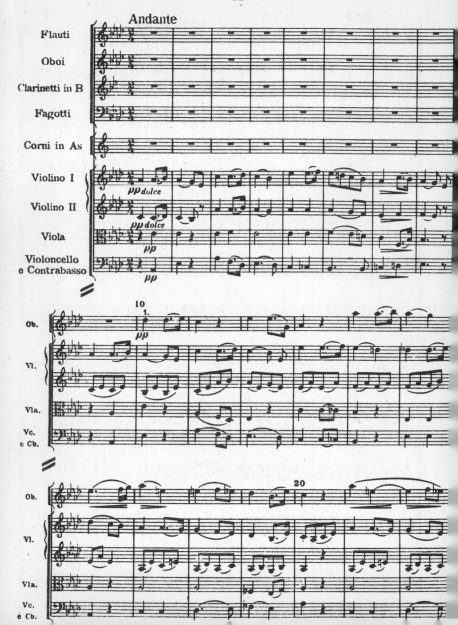

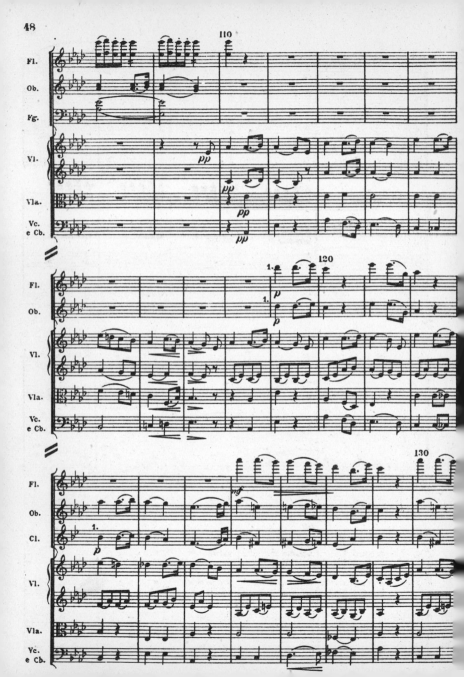

Menuetto, Allegro vivace

Menuetto D. C.

IV

68

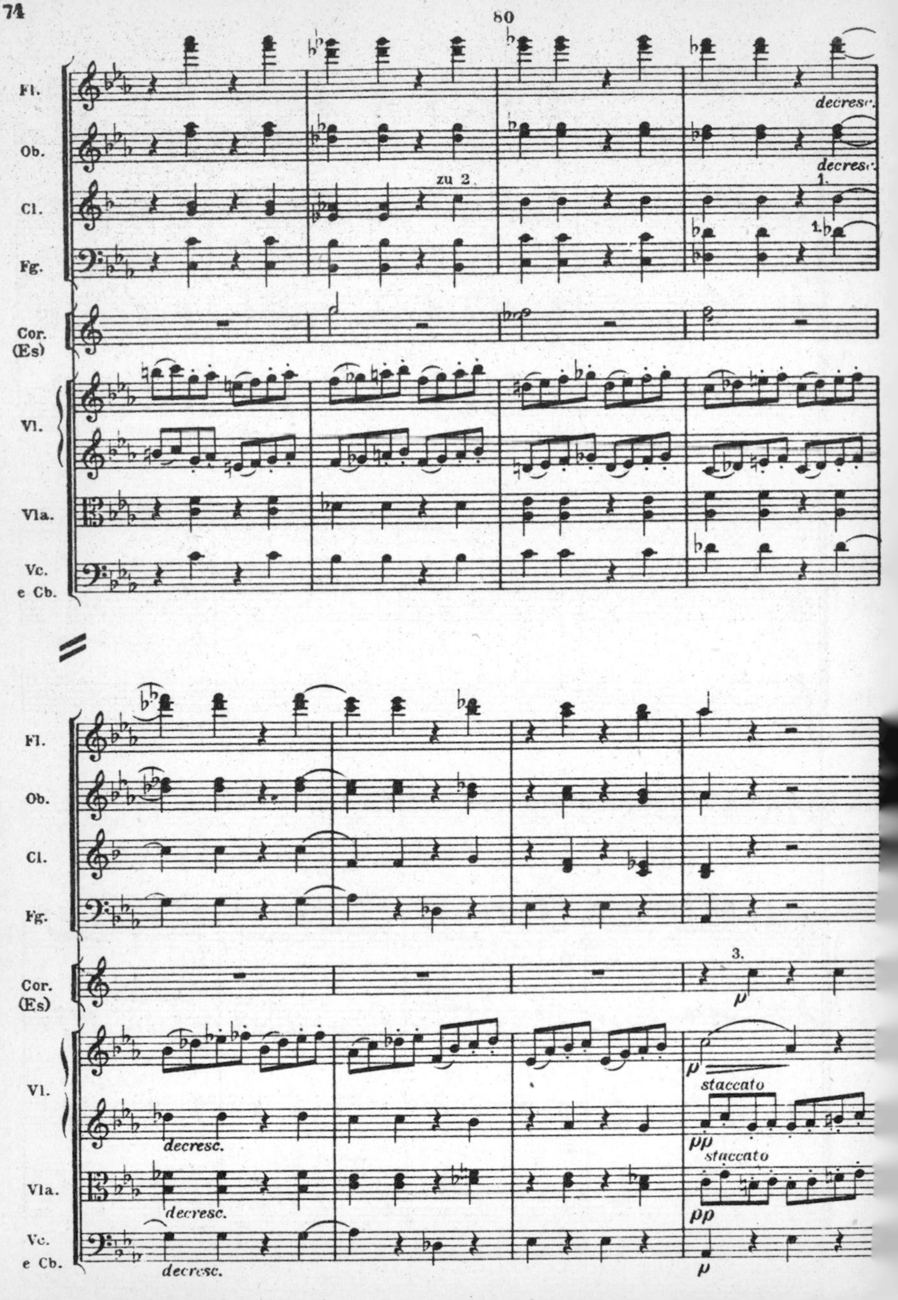
80
Fl.
Ob.
Cl.
Fg.
Cor. (Es)
Vl.
Vla.
Vc. e Cb.
zu 2
1.
decresc.
3.
p
pp
staccato

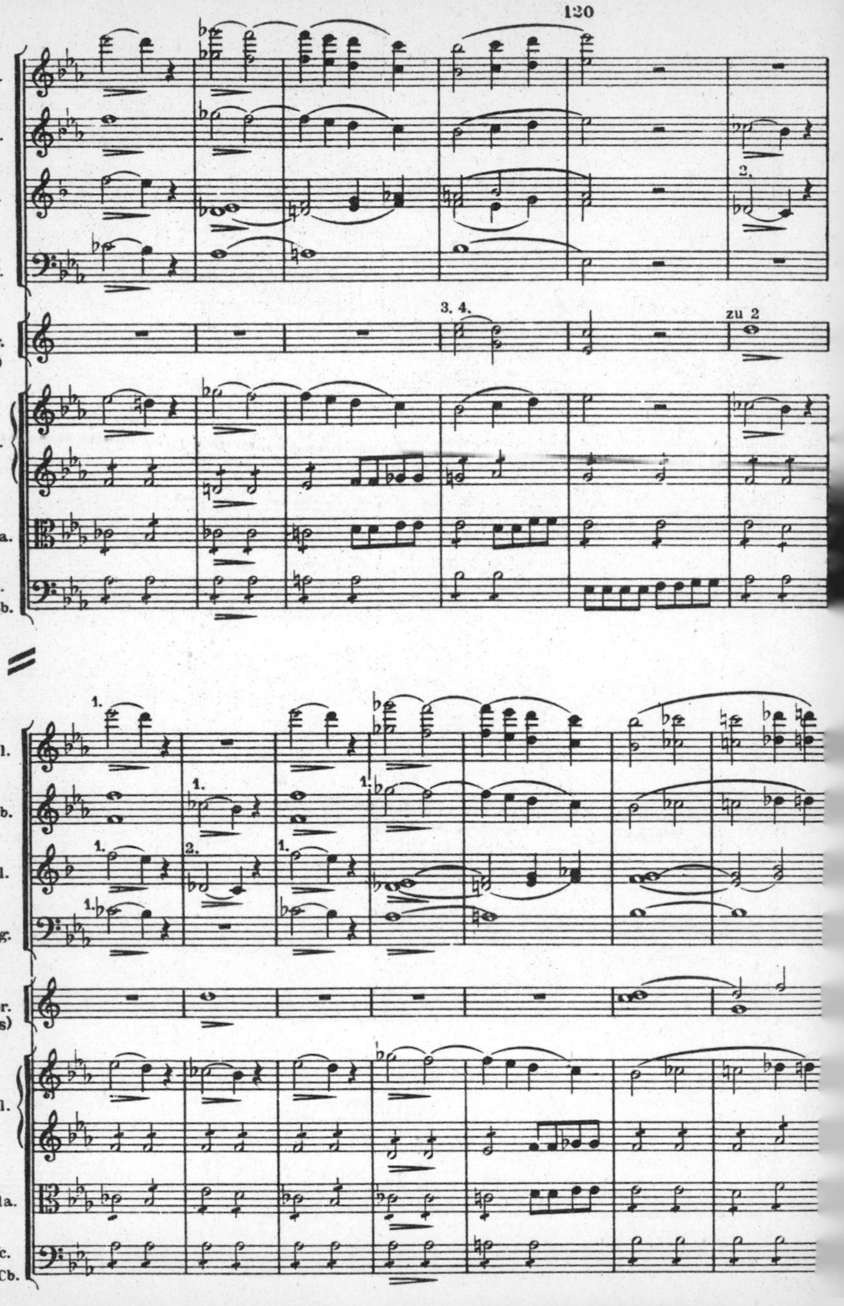
120
Fl.
Ob.
Cl.
Fg.
3. 4.
zu 2
Cor.
(Es)
Vl.
Vla.
Vc.
e Cb.

94

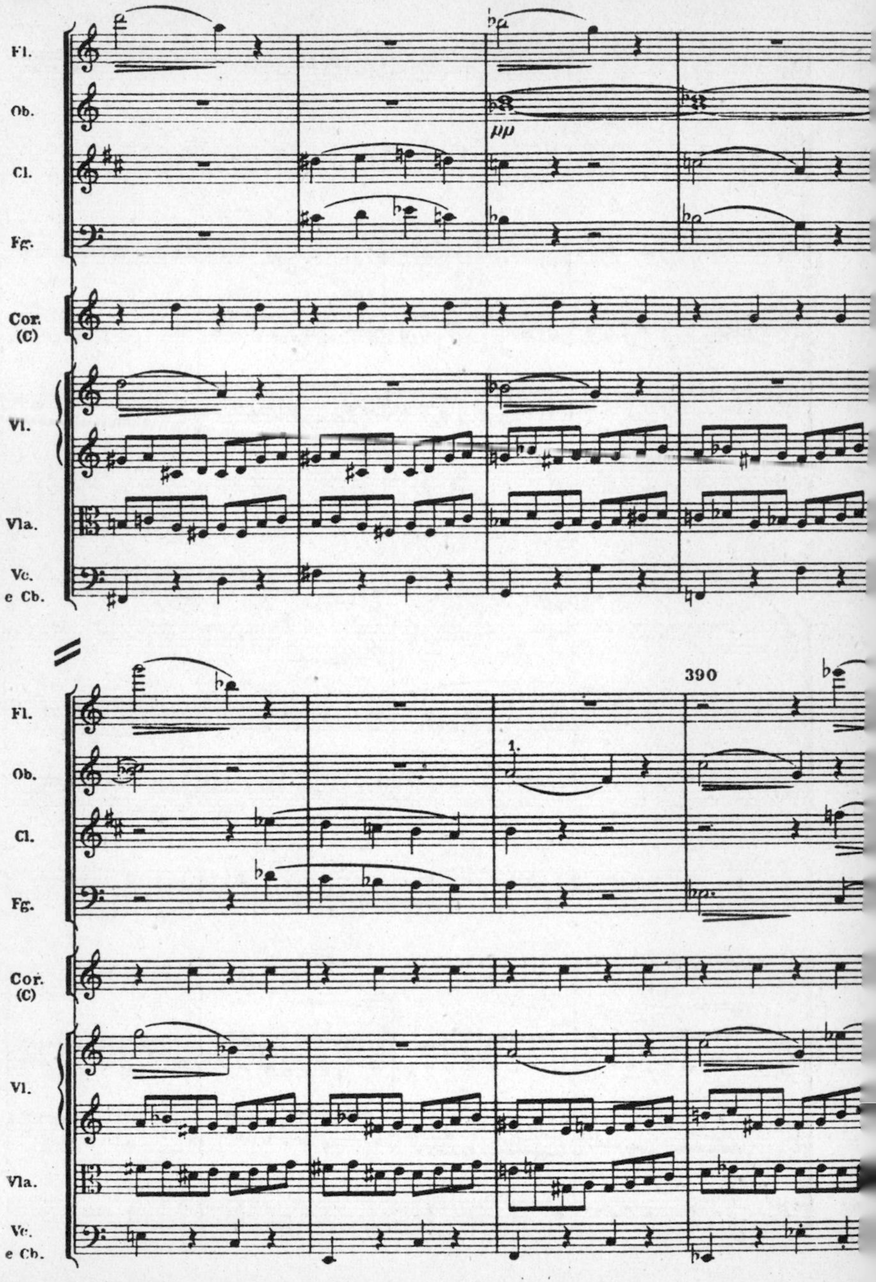
Fl.
Ob.
Cl.
Fg.
Cor. (C)
Vl.
Vla.
Vc. e Cb.
pp
390
1.

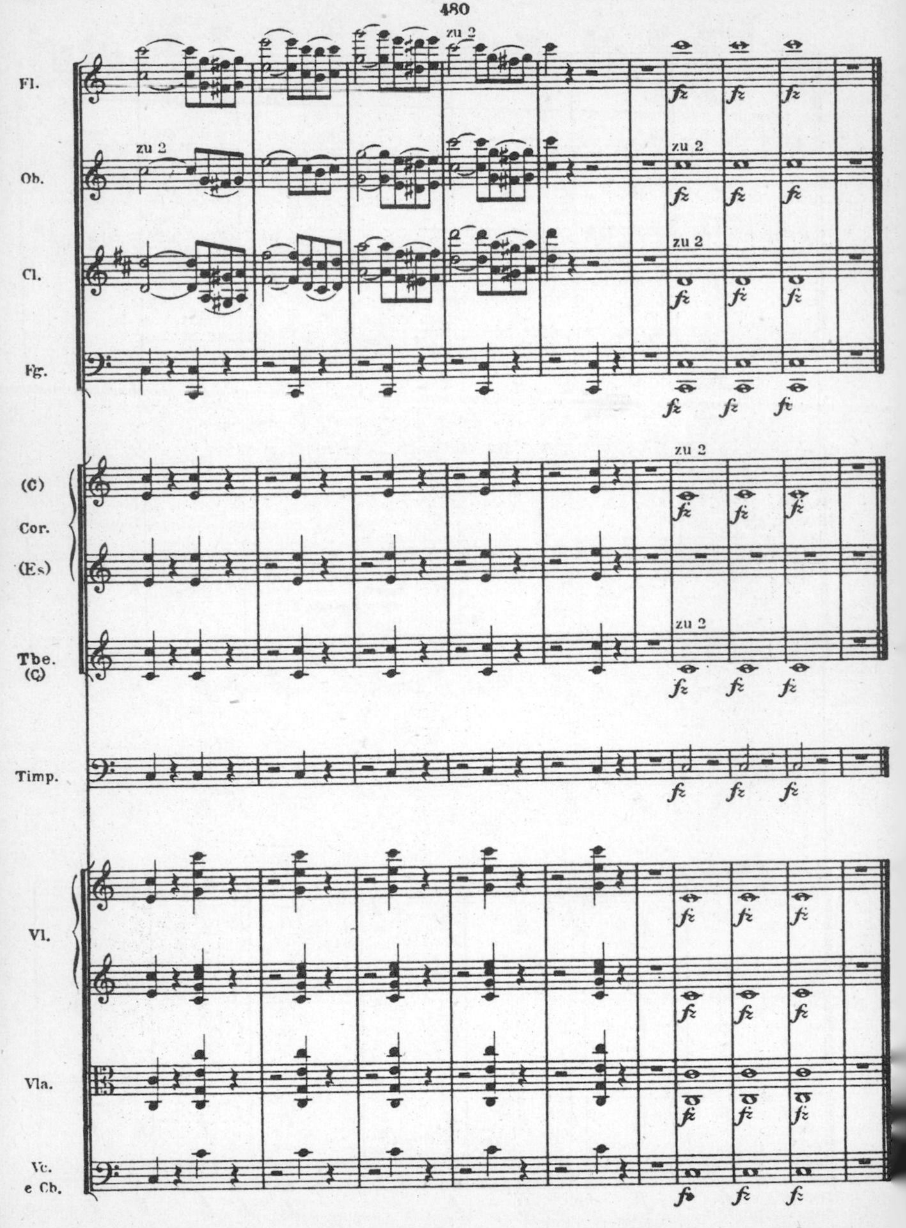
480
Fl.
zu 2
Ob.
Cl.
Fg.
(C)
Cor.
(Es)
Tbe.
(C)
Timp.
Vl.
Vla.
Vc.
e Cb.
fz

CHAMBER MUSIC

No.

299. Dvořák, Quartett, op. 51, Es . . . . .
300. Dvořák, Quartett, op. 61, C .
301. Dvořák, Quartett, op. 80, E . . . . .
302. Dvořák, Quartett, op. 96, F . . . . .
303. Dvořák, Quartett, op. 105, As . . . .
304. Dvořák, Quartett, op. 106, G . . . .
305. Dvořák, Klavier-Quintett, op.81, A .
306. Dvořák, Streich-Quintett, op. 97, Es .
307. Scontrino, Praeludium und Fuge, Em
308. Mozart, Serenade f. 8 Blasinstr., Es [375]
309. Mozart, Serenade f. 8 Blasinstr., Cm [388]
310. Bruckner, Streich-Quintett, F .
311. August Reuss, Quartett, op. 31, E .
312. Reger, Flöten-Trio (Seren.), op. 141a, G
313. Reger, Streich-Trio, op. 141 b, D m .
314. Reger, Quartett, op. 121, Fis m . . .
315. Klose, Quartett (Ein Tribut in 4 Raten), Es
316. Mendelssohn, Arnold, Quartett, op.87, D
317. Grieg, Quartett, F dur (unvollendet) .
318. Schönberg, Sextett (Verkl. Nacht) op. 4
319. Reger, Quartett, op. 74, D m . . . . .
320. Straesser, Quartett, op. 42, E m . . .
321. Scontrino, Quartett, F . . . .
322. Reger, Klarinetten-Quintett, op. 146, A
323. Franck, Quartett, D . . . .
324. Pfitzner, Klavier-Quintett, op. 23, C .
325. Suter, Sextett, op. 18, C . . . . . .
326. Suter, Quartett, op. 20, G . . . . . .
327. Andreae, Quartett, op. 33, E m . . .
328. Barblan, Quartett, op. 19, D . . . . .

No.

329. Franck, Klavier-Quintett, F m .
330. Dvořák, Klavier-Quartett, op. 87, Es .
331. Dvořák, Klavier-Trio, op. 65, F m .
332. Dvořák, Klav.-Trio, op. 90, Em (Dumky)
333. Reger, Klavier-Quartett, op. 133, A m
334. Schönberg, Quartett, op. 7, D m . .
335. Smetana, Klavier-Trio, op. 15, G m .
336. Reger, Klavier-Quintett, op. posth., C m
337. Dvořák, Sextett, op. 48, A . . . . .
338. Dvořák, Quintett, op. 77, G . . . .
339. Dohnányi, Quartett, op. 15, Des . .
340. Reger, Klavier-Quintett, op. 64, Cm .
341. Saint-Saëns, Klav.-Trio, op. 18, F . .
342. Saint-Saëns, Klav.-Quint., op. 14, A m
343. Dohnányi, Klav.-Quintett op. 26, Es m.
344. Nápravnik, Quartett, op. 16, E . .
345. Tscherepnin, Quartett, op. 11, A m .
346. Haas, Quartett, op. 32, C . . . . .
347. Mozart, Horn-Quintett, Es [407] . .
348. Corelli, Weihnachts-Konzert . . . .
349. Mozart, Divertimento No. 11, D [251] .
350. Graener, Quartett, op. 65, A m . . .
351. Mozart, Divertimento No. 13, F [253]
352. Mozart, Divertimento No. 14, B [270]
353. Schubert, Quartett, op. posth., D .
354. Schubert, Quartettsatz, op. posth. Cm
355. Haydn, Quartett, op. 77, 2. F . . .
356. Haydn, Quartett, op. 103, B . . . .
357. Corelli, Concerto grosso No. 1, D . .
358. Corelli, Concerto grosso No. 3, C m

OPERAS

901. **Wagner**, Rienzi . . . .
902. **Wagner**, Der fliegende Holländer .
903a.**Wagner**, Tannhäuser . . . . . .
903b.**Wagner**, Varianten d. Pariser Bearbg
904. **Wagner**, Lohengrin . . . .
905. **Wagner**, Tristan und Isolde . . .
906. **Wagner**, Meistersinger v. Nürnberg
907. **Wagner**, Rheingold . . . .
908. **Wagner**, Die Walküre . . . . . .
909. **Wagner**, Siegfried . . . .

910. **Wagner**, Götterdämmerung . . . .
911. **Wagner**, Parsifal . . . .
912. **Mozart**, Zauberflöte (H. Abert) . .
913. **Humperdinck**, Hänsel und Gretel
914. **Beethoven**, Fidelio . . . .
915. **Weber**, Der Freischütz (H. Abert) .
916. **Mozart**, Figaros Hochzeit (H. Abert)
917. **Gluck**, Iphigenie a. Tauris (H. Abert)
918. **Mozart**, Don Giovanni (A. Einstein)

CHORAL WORKS

951. **Beethoven**, Missa solemnis . . .
952. **Brahms**, Requiem (dtsch., frz., engl., it.)
953. **Bach**, Matthäus-Passion . . . . .
954. **Mozart**, Requiem . . . .
955. **Haydn**, Die Schöpfung . . . . . .
956. **Händel**, Der Messias . . . .
959. **Bach**, Hohe Messe, H moll . . . .
960. **Bruckner**, Te Deum . . . .
961. **Bruckner**, Große Messe, F moll . .
962. **Bach**, Weihnachtsoratorium . . .
963. **Palestrina**, Missa Papae Marcelli .
964. **Bach**, Magnificat (Schering) . . . .
965. **Bach**, Johannes-Passion . . . . .

966. **Palestrina**, Stabat Mater . . . .
967. **Bach**, Der zufriedengestellte Aeolus
968. **Reger**, Der 100. Psalm . . . . . .
969. **Brahms**, Requiem (Text deutsch) .
970. **Schubert**, Messe No. 6, Es . . .
971. **Bach**, Kaffee-Kantate . . . . . .
972. **Bruckner**, 150. Psalm . . . . . .
973. **Pergolesi**, Stabat Mater . . . . .
974. **Schubert**, Messe No. 5, As . . . .
975. **Verdi**, Requiem . . . .
976. **Schütz**, Matthäus-Passion . . . .
977. **Schütz**, Johannes-Passion . . . .

CANTATAS AND MOTETS

1001. **Bach**, No. 12: Weinen, Klagen . .
1002. **Bach**, No. 11: Lobet Gott (Himmelfahrtsorat.)
1003. **Bach**, No. 80: Ein' feste Burg . .
1004. **Bach**, No. 6: Bleib bei uns . . . .
1005. **Bach**, No. 161: Komm, du süße Todesstunde
1006. **Bach**, „Mer han en neue Oberkeet". Instr. von Felix Mottl . . . .
1007. **Bach**, No. 106: Gottes Zeit . . . .
1008. **Bach**, No. 56: Kreuzstab-Kantate .
1009. **Bach**, No. 79: Gott der Herr ist Sonn' u. Schild
1010. **Bach**, No. 54: Widerstehe doch der Sünde
1011. **Bach**, No. 4: Christ lag in Todesbanden .
1012. **Bach**, No. 1: Wie schön leuchtet der Morgenstern
1013. **Bach**, No. 34: O ewiges Feuer . .
1014. **Bach**, No. 81: Jesus schläft, was soll ich hoffen
1015. **Bach**, No. 85: Ich bin ein guter Hirt

1016. **Bach**, No. 31: Der Himmel lacht .
1017. **Bach**, No. 60: O Ewigkeit, du Donnerwort .
1018. **Bach**, No. 50: Nun ist das Heil . .
1019. **Bach**, No. 65: Sie werden aus Saba alle kommen . . . .
1020. **Bach**, No. 140: Wachet auf . . . .
1021. **Bach**, No. 55: Ich armer Mensch, ich Sündenknecht
1022. **Mozart**, Exultate jubilate . . . .
1023. **Bach**, No. 104: Du Hirte Israel .
1024. **Bach**, No. 182: Himmelskönig, sei willkommen
1025. **Bach**, No. 46: Schauet doch . . .
1026. **Bach**, No. 123: Liebster Emanuel
1027. **Bach**, No. 19: Es erhub sich . . .
1028. **Bach**, No. 8: Liebster Gott . . . .
1029. **Bach**, No. 21: Ich hatte viel Bekümmernis .
1030. **Bach**, No. 119: Preise, Jerusalem